Praise for *My Special Powers of the Universe*

"*My Special Powers of the Universe* is an enchanting book that discusses remarkable themes of helping children gain confidence. Libby Fairbairn is a stunning writer whose book is absolutely perfect as an educational tool for schools across the globe. As an educator with an MEd in International Teaching, I highly recommend this book for parents and educators across the world!"

> – Pashmina P.
> International Best-Selling Author of *The Cappuccino Chronicles Trilogy* and
> *What is a Gupsey?*

"Libby Fairbairn is a wonderful author who captures the spiritual nuance of cultivating confidence for children. Practices from many masters can be seen in her writing, and definitely resonates as the perfect book for any family who loves teaching their children about their special powers. I highly recommend this book!"

> – Judy O'Beirn,
> International Best-Selling Author of *Unwavering Strength Series*,
> Founder and President, Hasmark Publishing International

"This book is a must-have for all. I love how Elisabeth Fairbairn explains in an age-appropriate way how the power of affirmations and believing in yourself can not only benefit how we navigate life, but how we handle situations that may come up in our every day. *My Special Powers of the Universe* is an important book for any child's collection."

> – Kelly Vurinaris, International Best-Selling Author of *Hi, I'm Me*

"WOW! What a special, beautifully written and powerful book Elisabeth has created here. This is exactly what our kids need, and Elisabeth has masterfully created this book that is the first of what will be an incredibly important series. The greatest gift that we can all give our children, apart from love, is the gift of awareness. An understanding of how their minds work and how to use it to create happiness and success across all aspects of their lives. As many of us aren't even aware of these Universal powers ourselves, it's great that we now have access to this book and it's profound lessons, so that we too can learn and grow as we read this book with our kids. I particularly love the story on mentorship and how the kid who helps William is called Bob, the name of my most amazing and wise personal mentor, Bob Proctor. I'm grateful for this book and can't wait for the next ones of the series. Well done Elisabeth!"

> – Dr Spencer Pool
> Bob Proctor's Top 1% Consultant

MY SPECIAL POWERS OF THE UNIVERSE

Stories to help your child gain
a positive outlook of the universe

BY ELISABETH FAIRBAIRN

 Hasmark
PUBLISHING
INTERNATIONAL

Published by
Hasmark Publishing
www.hasmarkpublishing.com

Copyright © 2020
First Edition

Disclaimer

Permission should be addressed in writing to elisabethfairbairn@gmail.com

Illustrations: Matrix Solutions

Editor: Kathryn Young
kathryn@hasmarkpublishing.com

Cover and Book Design: Anne Karklins
anne@hasmarkpublishing.com

ISBN 13: 978-1-989756-26-3
ISBN 10: 1989756263

For my amazing family for always believing in me.
And especially for Ally –
I grow and learn every day because of you.
I love you mostest on toastest.

Dear Parents

With so many challenges and competing priorities in today's
modern world, helping our children to be resilient, true to themselves,
and emotionally intelligent has never been more important.

Lessons of personal awareness, the powers of the universe,
and affirmations are racing through the adult world.
This series brings those lessons to life for children.

Each story ends with the thought behind it and a suggested affirmation.

You know your child best and what works for him or her.
Choose your favorite affirmation and practice it together.
Or make your own affirmation!
You'll be amazed at how both your lives may change.

Happy reading and warm wishes to all.

Table of Contents

THE POWER OF BELIEF

It was spring, and Daisy was looking forward to creating a wonderful garden next to her house.

This was the first time she had worked on her garden, so she went to the garden centre to get some advice and seeds. She chose some wonderful seeds that would grow yummy fruits and vegetables and some beautiful flowers that would make people smile.

She wasn't sure her effort would work,
so she only bought half of what she needed.
The helpful shop keeper warned her,
"Make sure you sow good seeds everywhere.
Soil doesn't choose flowers over weeds.
It grows what you sow. And if you sow nothing,
the weeds will grow in its space."
But Daisy didn't think this was right.
If she did nothing to half of the garden,
she thought it would just stay empty.

Back in her garden, she tended to half of the soil. She sowed the seeds. She sang to the growing seedlings. She told them how wonderful they looked and how good they were going to taste. As time passed, she beheld a beautiful garden that made her smile and feel healthy and happy.

But Daisy neglected the other half of the garden. With no positivity and no attention, weeds took hold of the garden.

When Daisy saw this, she felt sad. The shop keeper had been right! And what was worse, the weeds started to work their way into the loved part. The weeds often seemed stronger than the flowers. The flowers needed a lot more attention to grow and be healthier than the weeds.

Daisy had two choices: give in to the weeds or make the effort to remove the weeds, take away the negative roots, and replace them with flowers. It wasn't easy. It took work every day. But Daisy knew it was worth it, as she was happy and healthy every day and brought love and smiles to everyone around her.

THE POWER OF BELIEF

Your subconscious mind grows
what you sow, so feed it
positive thoughts every day.

SUGGESTED AFFIRMATION
TO SAY EVERY DAY:

I am safe, I am loved,
I can be anything
I want to be.

THE POWER
OF PERSISTENCE

One day, Flippy and Fred found themselves in a Baker's kitchen. The Baker had gone home for the day, and the little frogs were having a look around to see what they could see.

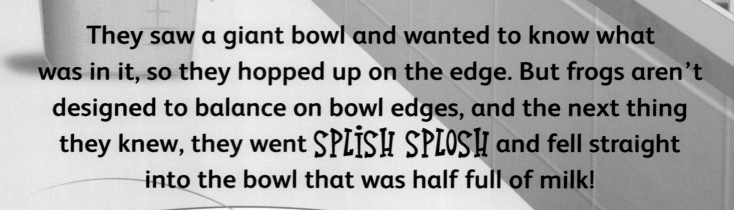

They saw a giant bowl and wanted to know what was in it, so they hopped up on the edge. But frogs aren't designed to balance on bowl edges, and the next thing they knew, they went SPLISH SPLOSH and fell straight into the bowl that was half full of milk!

Flippy and Fred were frightened. They couldn't reach the top of the bowl, and the sides were too slippery for them to climb up. They kept swimming while thinking about what they could do.

They started to get tired. Fred said, "There isn't anything I can do. I'm really tired. I'm going to stop swimming." Flippy was upset by this and tried to tell Fred to keep trying. "You can't give up, Fred. We just have to keep trying." But Fred stopped swimming, rolled onto his back, and closed his eyes. Flippy, however, refused to give up. He kept swimming…

And swimming

And swimming

And swimming

And swimming

As Flippy carried on all alone, he felt his legs getting tired, and the milk was getting harder and harder to swim in.

In the morning, Flippy awoke to the sound of the baker opening the door. He wasn't sure when he'd fallen asleep, but he looked down and saw what all his effort had done to the milk. He was sitting on top of a lump of butter! He shook Fred awake, and they quickly hopped to the edge of the bowl and out of the window.

THE POWER OF PERSISTENCE

Keep trying. Persist. When things are tough,
just put one foot in front of another and keep going.
No one gets anywhere standing still.

SUGGESTED AFFIRMATION TO SAY EVERY DAY:

I can achieve anything
when I keep trying.
I get up each time I fall.
I get stronger every day.

THE POWER
OF MENTORSHIP

One day, William was walking along
the street, and he fell into a big hole.
The sides were steep, and there was no ladder!

He saw his doctor walk by,
and he called out to him.
"Hey, Doctor Smith, can you help me?
I'm stuck in this hole, and I
can't see how to get out!"
The doctor looked down,
thought for a second,
wrote William a prescription,
and dropped it down the hole.
Then he carried on
with his journey.

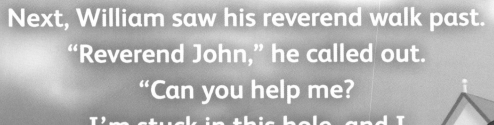

Next, William saw his reverend walk past.
"Reverend John," he called out.
"Can you help me?
I'm stuck in this hole, and I
can't see how to get out!"
Reverend John looked down.
"Oh, bless you, William,
what a pickle to be in!
Here you go!" And he wrote
out a prayer and
dropped it into the hole.

William was starting to feel sad, but he couldn't give up.
Soon he saw his friend walk by.
"Bob, Bob!" he called out. "Bob, can you help me?
I'm stuck in this hole and can't see how to get out!"

Bob looked down, saw William, and jumped into the hole.
William was shocked! "Oh, Bob! What are you doing?
Now we are both stuck down here!"

But Bob smiled. "I've been down here before, William, and I know the way out." William listened to Bob and followed him, and before long, they were both out of the hole.

THE POWER OF MENTORSHIP

Seek sources of wisdom and success in your life and follow them.

SUGGESTED AFFIRMATION TO SAY EVERY DAY:

I attract loving, honest, wonderful mentors in my life. I grow by choosing to learn from the best role models in life.

THE POWER
OF AWARENESS

Alvin the Ant was out foraging for food.
He was using a path he'd used before,
but he didn't see the new crack that had
appeared in the ground. He fell in.
It was dark and not very nice. He felt scared.
It wasn't his fault. It took him ages to
find his way out and carry on with his journey.

The next day, Alvin was out foraging again,
and he walked down the same path.
He pretended not to see the crack. As you can
imagine, he fell back down the crack!
It was still scary and not nice. He couldn't believe
he had ended up there again. It took him ages
to get back out and carry on with his journey.

The following day, Alvin was out once again foraging for food. He saw the crack in the path, but now he fell in out of habit! Poor Alvin! He knew he could only blame himself on this one, but he quickly got himself out of the hole this time and then carried on with his journey.

The following day, Alvin was again out foraging for food. He saw the crack, and this time he walked around it. His journey was a lot quicker that day.

But the next day, he went out foraging for food, and this time, he chose a different path.

THE POWER OF AWARENESS

Learn who you are and how you feel and recognize when it is time to change to a better path.

SUGGESTED AFFIRMATION
TO SAY EVERY DAY:

I am so glad I know
how I feel and how
I can change to be
the best me.

About the Author

Elisabeth is a mum to a wonderful seven-year-old daughter, Alyssa. The journey to a healthy, happy child was not smooth. With Ally being so excited to join the world, she came along at an early twenty-five weeks weighing less than a bag of sugar.

In her day job, Elisabeth is an experienced nurse, but nothing prepares anyone for parenthood, let alone parenting such an incredibly tiny vulnerable baby.

As a nurse, Elisabeth knows the importance of not just the physical but also the emotional nourishment for Ally, and she started learning and researching all about different child-rearing theories. This coupled well with taking on a teaching job at work. Because of her various roles – as mummy, nurse, educator – she recognises the importance and value of children learning skills such as emotional resilience, strength of character and mind, and much more.

With a passion for improving the lives of those around her, she started a health and wellbeing business and set to work writing children's books to bring wonderful stories with morals and meanings to as many people as she could.

HEARTS to be HEARD

Giving a Voice to Creativity!

With every donation, a voice will be given to
the creativity that lies within the hearts of
our children living with diverse challenges.

By making this difference, children that may
not have been given the opportunity to have their
Heart Heard will have the freedom to create
beautiful works of art and musical creations.

Donate by visiting

HeartstobeHeard.com

We thank you.

Printed in Great Britain
by Amazon